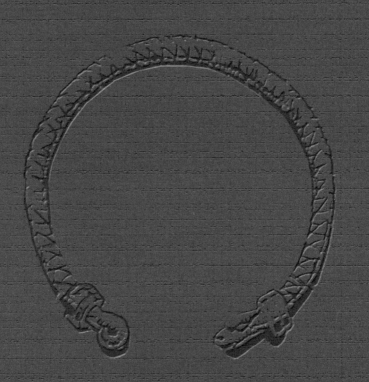

Dave Gibbons:
Writer

John Higgins:
Artist

Colored by:
Jonny Rench
WildStorm FX (#5)

Lettered by Todd Klein

Original series covers
by Dave Gibbons,
colored by John Higgins

Jim Lee, Editorial Director
John Nee, VP—Business Development
Scott Dunbier, Executive Editor
Kristy Quinn, Assistant Editor
Ed Roeder, Art Director
Paul Levitz, President & Publisher
Georg Brewer, VP—Design & DC Direct Creative
Richard Bruning, Senior VP—Creative Director
Patrick Caldon, Executive VP—Finance & Operations
Chris Caramalis, VP—Finance
John Cunningham, VP—Marketing
Terri Cunningham, VP—Managing Editor
Alison Gill, VP—Manufacturing
Hank Kanalz, VP—General Manager, WildStorm
Paula Lowitt, Senior VP—Business & Legal Affairs
MaryEllen McLaughlin, VP—Advertising & Custom Publishing
Gregory Noveck, Senior VP—Creative Affairs
Sue Pohja, VP—Book Trade Sales
Cheryl Rubin, Senior VP—Brand Management
Jeff Trojan, VP—Business Development, DC Direct
Bob Wayne, VP—Sales

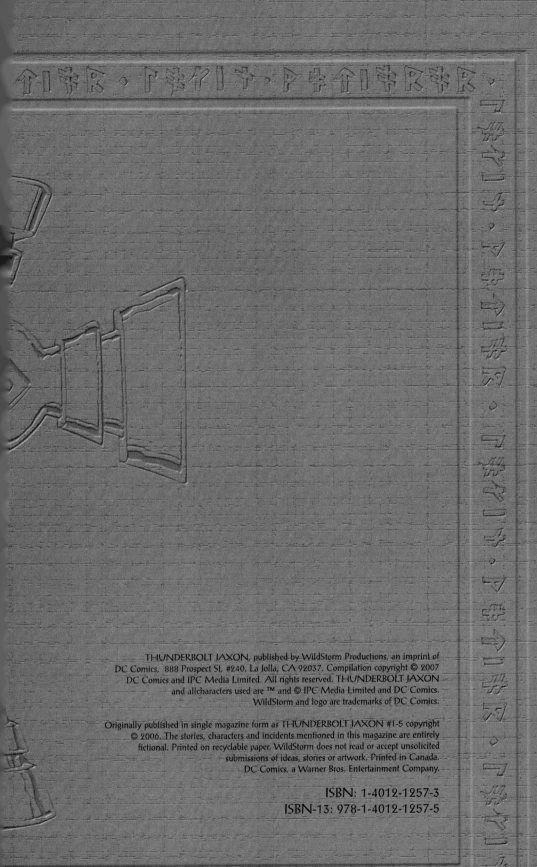

THUNDERBOLT JAXON, published by WildStorm Productions, an imprint of
DC Comics, 888 Prospect St, #240, La Jolla, CA 92037. Compilation copyright © 2007
DC Comics and IPC Media Limited. All rights reserved. THUNDERBOLT JAXON
and all characters used are ™ and © IPC Media Limited and DC Comics.
WildStorm and logo are trademarks of DC Comics.

Originally published in single magazine form as THUNDERBOLT JAXON #1-5 copyright
© 2006. The stories, characters and incidents mentioned in this magazine are entirely
fictional. Printed on recyclable paper. WildStorm does not read or accept unsolicited
submissions of ideas, stories or artwork. Printed in Canada.
DC Comics, a Warner Bros. Entertainment Company.

ISBN: 1-4012-1257-3
ISBN-13: 978-1-4012-1257-5

KNOCKOUT ANNUAL 1960

THUNDERBOLT JAXON

Although I have only the dimmest memories of reading *Thunderbolt Jaxon* way back when, it's the name that really stuck with me. Sounding almost like some clunky old cowboy or heavyweight boxer, it was the "x" that really made him memorable. That and the skirt.

Yes, skirt. Bewildering to me, even then, was why the re-incarnation of a Norse god—mighty Thor, no less—should be wearing a girly skirt. I can only suppose that editorial wires got crossed and the artist used some Greek god as his reference. Anyway, Jaxon was such a great brute that no one in his strips ever drew attention to it. Not that Jaxon was a bully. Far from it, he had much of the good-natured charm of the original Captain Marvel. Which was appropriate, given their shared boy-into-muscleman-via-lightning-bolt schtick. However, in Jaxon's case, it was a magic belt that did the trick rather than a magic word. A magic belt with no fewer than FOURTEEN magic words on its buckle:

HERE COMES THUNDERBOLT JAXON

"When this belt is on you tight,
Fight for right with all your might!"

Shazam? Pah!

British comics have not traditionally had much success with superheroes and Jaxon was no exception. His appearances were spotty, and he never became more than a supporting act. Debuting in Comet in August 1949, under the editorship of Ted Holmes, his early adventures were drawn by Hugh McNeill, from scripts by an unknown writer. Jaxon later turned up in *Knockout*, drawn by Ian Kennedy, later to become the doyen of *Air Ace Picture Library*. Some of Jaxon's adventures were recycled in *Buster* in the sixties, his name re-lettered, in an even more bewildering,

religion-melding twist, as "Johnny Samson." The height of his visibility was probably on the cover of the *Knockout Annual* for 1960.

Perhaps it was the skirt, after all.

Somebody very like Jaxon turned up years later in Grant Morrison's *Zenith*, but didn't last long. Suffice to say his belt failed to activate and he died. Well, it was the eighties.

Anyway, when I saw the list of characters eligible for updating as part of the ALBION line, it was Jaxon's name that leapt out at me. The aforementioned "boy-into-muscleman-via-lightning-bolt schtick" seemed a good comic book archetype to have some fun with and putting Jaxon into today's Britain seemed an interesting challenge.

When my old WATCHMEN buddy John Higgins expressed an interest in drawing the new version, I knew we were set. John's feel for character, atmosphere, location and humor make him the perfect fit for Jaxon.

He's always had a good eye for a skirt, too.

— Dave Gibbons

the unbinding

'SCUSE ME.

YOUNGSTERS TODAY.

ALWAYS IN A HURRY.

BE THERE SOON ENOUGH.

IS THAT *YOU*, JACK? IT'S BILLY.

YOU SOUND A BIT *FUNNY*.

I'M--ALL RIGHT.

YOU?

I FEEL *REALLY GOOD*. THIS CHEMO MUST BE *WORKING* AT LAST.

YOU SOUND LIKE YOU CAUGHT A *COLD* IN ALL THAT RAIN. ANYWAY...

...I LOOKED THAT *WEIRD WRITING* UP ON THE *INTERNET*. YOU KNOW, OFF THAT *STONE*. IT'S *SAXON*. REALLY *OLD*. FOURTH CENTUR--

BILLY...?

I'M *OFF* NOW, SON. DON'T BE UP TOO *LATE* ON THAT THING. YOU NEED YOUR *REST*. SEE YOU IN THE MORNING.

YEAH, YEAH. *SEE* YOU.

YOU *THERE*, JACK?

SORRY. MY *DAD*, OFF TO WORK. ANYWAY...

...I NEED TO DO A *PROPER* SEARCH, BUT IT SAYS SOMETHING ABOUT *GODS*. NOT *JESUS* AND ALL THAT. *NORSE* GODS.

JACK? YOU THERE?

YEAH. I'M...G-*GODS*, YOU SAID?

NORSE GODS. PEOPLE 'ROUND HERE USED TO *BELIEVE* IN THEM. THEN THE *CHRISTIANS* TOOK OVER.

THAT *STONE* SAYS THEY TOOK THE GODS' *TREASURES* AWAY. LIKE THEY WERE *REAL*.

THEN THEY *BURIED* THE TREASURE ON *HALLOWED GROUND*, SO THE GODS COULDN'T *GET* THEM. I'LL SEND YOU THE *PICTURE*.

BUT THAT'S NOT *ALL*. THAT *BELT*, IT--

RRRRR-RRGH

QUIET, BOY. YOU'LL BE TASTING *FLESH* SOON ENOUGH.

EVENING, MR. O'DUNNE.

ONLY ONE SENTRY. TOOK *CARE* OF HIM, NO PROBLEM.

STILL PLENTY OF *SLAUGHTER* TO COME, LADS.

MIND *FENRIR* A MOMENT, LARRY.

AND MIND YOU DON'T GET BETWEEN HIM AND HIS *DINNER.*

THIEVING LITTLE #%!$S...

⇒beep⇐

COME *ON* COME *ON* ANSWER THE F--

BILLY?

OH, HELLO, *BILLY.* IT'S *LARRY.* YOU KNOW, *JACK'S STEPDAD.* HOW ARE *YOU?*

NO, *JACK'S* ALL RIGHT. ME AND HIS *MUM* JUST NEED TO *SEE* YOU.

I'LL TELL YOU WHEN WE *GET* THERE.

INKERMAN ROAD, ISN'T IT? REMIND ME, WHAT WAS THE *NUMBER* AGAIN?

WHO'S THERE? I *SAID*--

SAF. IT'S *ME,* JACK.

I'VE GOT TO *TALK* TO YOU.

QUIET, JACK. MUM AND DAD ARE ON MY CASE ENOUGH *ALREADY.*

WELL, LET ME *IN,* THEN.

IT'S F-*FREEZING* OUT HERE.

SO WHY'D YOU COME OUT IN A *BLIZZARD?* YOU COULD'VE *TEXTED* ME...

LOST MY *PHONE.*

IT'S THAT--THAT *TREASURE* WE FOUND. SOMETHING *WEIRD'S* GOING ON.

WEIRD?

I--I PUT THIS *BELT* ON AND I TURNED INTO... SOMEONE *ELSE.* THEN I HAD THIS *DREAM...*

THEN MY *STEPDAD* CHANGED, TOO. JUST FOR A *MOMENT...*

YEAH, *RIIIGHT.*

ARE YOU *PRANKING* ME, JACK?

NO. THE BELT *DID* CHANGE ME. I HAD THESE *MUSCLES* AND *LONG HAIR* AND--

PROVE IT, THEN. PUT IT ON *AGAIN.* GO ON, *JACK,* I'VE GOTTA SEE *THIS.*

NO. NO, LOOK, I'M REALLY *SCARED,* SAF. REALLY SC--

SAFFRON? WHAT ARE YOU *DOING?*

WATCHING TELLY.

WELL, TURN IT *OFF.* YOU NEED YOUR *SLEEP,* MY GIRL.

AND I *HOPE* YOU WAKE UP IN A BETTER *MOOD.*

LOOK, I'M TAKING THE *BELT* 'ROUND BILLY'S. HE'S FOUND OUT A BIT *ABOUT* IT. YOU *COMING?*

YEAH, ALL RIGHT.

I LIKE *SNOW.*

AND I'M *SICK* OF *THIS* PLACE.

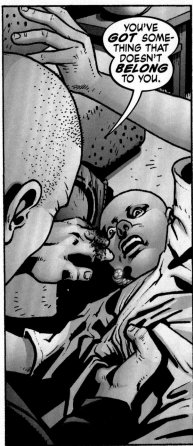

FIRST, WE GET OUR **OWN** 'OUSE STRAIGHT.

COME **ON** NOW, GALP. ENOUGH **LYIN'** AROUND. HELP YOUR **BROTHERS.**

BUT IT REALLY **HURTS**, DAD. MORE THAN THE **LAST** TIME AND IT AIN'T **CLOSIN'** AS QUICK.

ENOUGH **EXCUSES**, YOU LAZY **LUMP.** YOU'LL **LIVE.** YOU ALWAYS **DO.** NOW GET OUT THERE AND **HELP.**

ALL RIGHT, DAD. BUT I AIN'T **HEALIN'** LIKE I **USETA.**

I'M GONNA **HURT** ONE OF O'DUNNE'S BOYS **BAD** FOR THIS.

WE'RE GONNA 'URT **ALL** OF 'EM BAD, GALP.

'URT 'EM WHERE THEY **LIVE.**

"USELESS TO *STRUGGLE*, WHELP.

"THE *ROPES* WILL ONLY HURT YOU *MORE*.

YOU HAVE A *STORY* TO TELL. OR IS YOUR *TONGUE* TIED, TOO?

PRIVATE. KEEP OUT.

JUST LEAVE IT TO *ME*, MR. O'DUNNE. I'LL *BEAT* IT OUT OF HER.

NO. NOT *YET*, LARRY.

I'LL TALK TO HER FIRST. YOU GO AND GET YOURSELF A DRINK...

YOU DON'T KNOW WHAT THIS IS ALL ABOUT, DO YOU, WHELP?

OR WHO WE ARE.

HMM.

DO YOU LIKE STORIES, WHELP?

STOP CALLING ME A WHELP, WHATEVER IT IS.

HAH. IT DOES TALK.

LISTEN. I'LL TELL YOU A STORY.

MAYBE MY WORDS WILL HELP YOUR OWN TO FLOW.

"AND IF YOUR WORDS DO NOT, THEN YOUR BLOOD WILL."

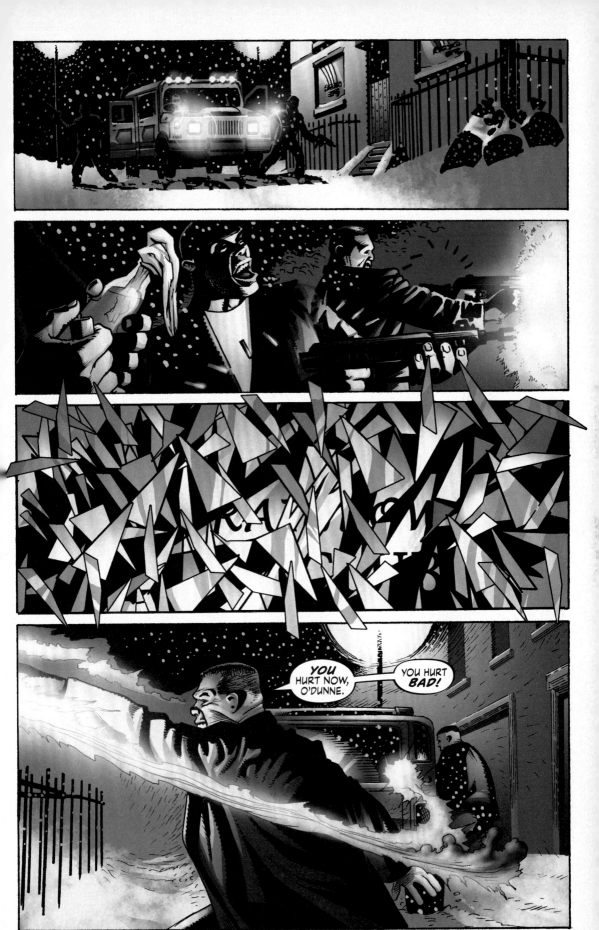

YOU KNOW, MAYBE WE *SHOULD* GO TO THE *POLICE*...

FORGET *THEM.* THEY WON'T HELP *US.*

AND WE CAN'T...GO *HOME.*

WHOOH!

ANYWAY, I THOUGHT WE *AGREED.*

WE'RE TAKING THESE THINGS *BACK* TO WHERE WE *FOUND* THEM.

BURYING THEM. ON *HALLOWED GROUND.* LEAVE EVERYTHING LIKE IT *WAS* BEFORE.

IF--IF IT'S NOT TOO *LATE* FOR THAT...

FIRST *BUS* TO THAT RUINED CHURCH IS DUE OUT *ANY MINUTE*...

BETTER *HURRY*, THEN. HERE, JACK--YOU WANT TO HAVE *THIS*?

I--I DON'T EVEN WANT TO *TOUCH* IT...

IF...*HE* TAKES ME *OVER* AGAIN...I MIGHT NOT BE ABLE TO...TO COME *BACK.*

I DON'T WANT TO D-*DIE.*

NO ONE'S GOING TO *DIE*, JACK.

YEAH. 'SPECIALLY NOT *THEM*, BACK AT THE *GARAGE.*

IS SHE...?

DON'T *WORRY*, JACK. SHE'S--

SHE'S FINE. NOW LET'S GET *OFF* HERE.

UHN. BIBT BY TUNG...

THAT'S THE CHURCH DOWN THERE.

C'MON. WE HAVE TO PUT THE *TREASURE* OUT OF THEIR REACH.

THERE GO THE BRATS.

I *SEE* THEM, LARRY. THEY'RE *FAST*--

--BUT NOT AS FAST AS *FENRIR!*

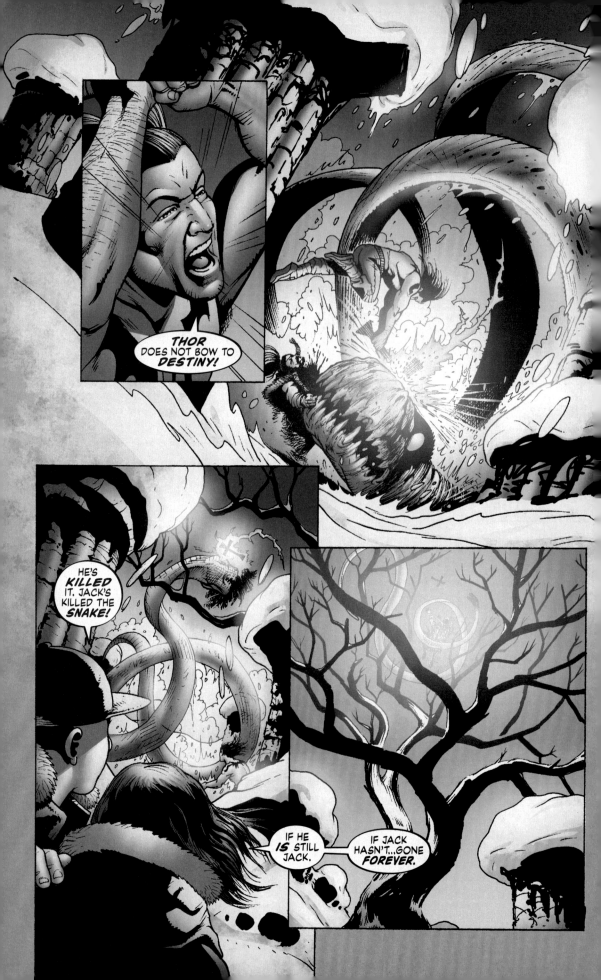

the end...
for now.

THUNDER BOLT JAXON

#1: the unbinding

THUNDER BOLT JAXON

#2: the Quickening

THUNDER BOLT JAXON

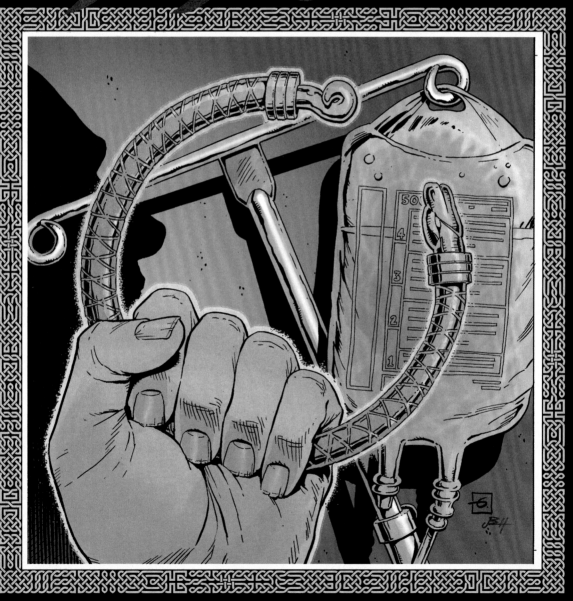

#3: the Bargain

THUNDER BOLT
JaXon

#4: In Fire and Ice

THUNDER BOLT JAXON

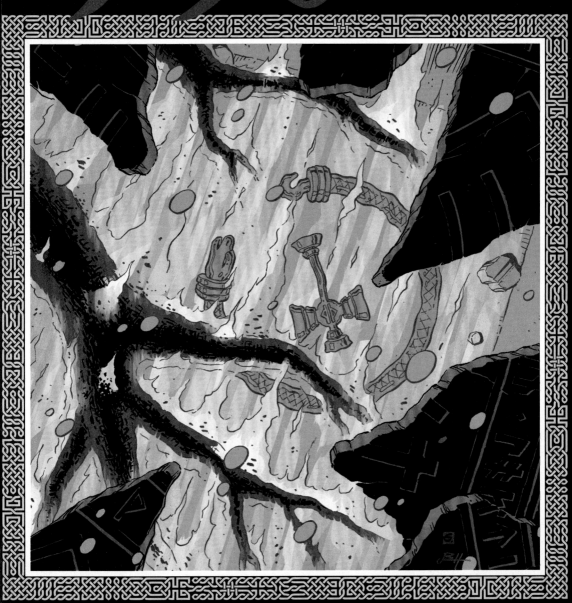

#5: RAGNAROK

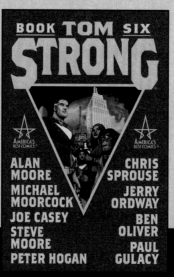
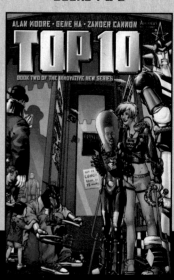